T0298183

Meet big **M** and little **m**.

Trace each letter with your finger and say its name.

M is for

monster

M is also for

mouse

mean

mittens

mug

Mm Story

On a snowy day in **M**arch,
a **m**ouse **m**et a **m**onster.

At first, the **m**ouse thought the **m**onster was **m**ean.

Then, the **m**onster gave
the **m**ouse a pair
of cozy **m**ittens.

Next, the **m**onster **m**ade him a **m**ug of hot chocolate with **m**arshmallows. **M**mmmm!

7

That **m**ouse was **m**istaken.
The **m**onster was NOT **m**ean.
She was **m**arvelous!